THE OFFICIAL
GARFIELD
ANNUAL

Created by
JIM DAVIS

Written by
Gordon Volke

£5.25

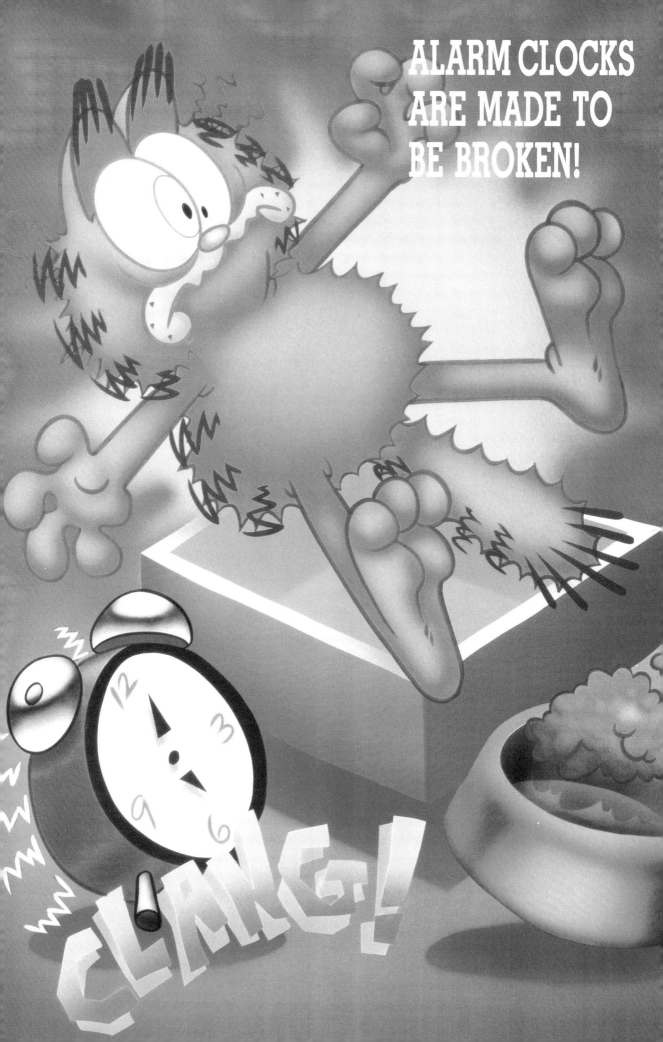

The HIPPIE HIPPIE SHAKE-UP

"Look at all those yo-yos, Odie," called Garfield, pointing out of the window one Monday morning. Odie wagged his tail excitedly.
"Not yo-yos with strings, you bonebrain," cried Garfield. "I mean *yo-yo* yo-yos!"
Odie looked totally baffled, so Garfield pressed his nose against the glass.
"People going to work!" he exclaimed. "Believers in the work ethic. YO-YOS!"

Garfield and Odie pulled funny faces at the commuters and shopkeepers hurrying to and fro outside the house. Nobody took any notice — they were all too busy trying to get to work on time. Then Jon came in. He was wearing a vivid floral kaftan and a set of wooden beads around his neck.
"A great improvement," commented Garfield. "You're only thirty years out of date now."
"I'm not going to work today, boys," announced Jon. "In fact, I'm not going to work ever again. I've given it up. I don't believe in the work ethic any more. It's for yo-yos!"
"I do the jokes around here," grumbled Garfield.

Jon led Garfield and Odie outside.

"We're going travelling," he announced. "I've traded in the car for a coach that has everything we need in life."

"Coffee machine, air-conditioning, TV above every seat?" enquired Garfield.

"Rolled matresses and a one-ring stove," said Jon, pointing to a battered old bus with swirling shapes painted along the side. He pushed his pets on board and clambered into the driving seat.

"Say good-bye to the shackles of the past!" cried Jon, making the ancient engine splutter into life.

"You mean to civilisation as we know it," muttered Garfield.

The bus bumped and rattled its way out of town. Garfield sat on the back seat, scowling like a gargoyle, while Odie looked unhappily out of the window.

"Regretting all the lampposts we're passing, eh Odie?" said Garfield. Eventually, Jon brought the bus to a shuddering halt outside a cafe.

"Time for a drink," he called.

Garfield shot down the bus faster than Linford Christie pursued by a swarm of hunting wasps.

"I'll have a cola float with triple ice-cream, cherries, sliced peaches and chopped nuts on top," he whooped.

"Fetch some water, Garfield," said Jon, holding out a bucket and pointing to a stream on the other side of the road.

Garfield looked aghast.

"Only lower life-forms like dogs drink water!" he protested.

"We're living off the land now, Garfield," explained Jon. "The best things in life are free."

"Close, but no banana," growled Garfield, snatching the bucket. "The best things in life are *food* !"

The travellers continued their bus journey. As juddering afternoon gave way to bone-rattling evening, Garfield began to get desperate.

"Well, this has been a fun day out," he cried, grabbing the steering wheel of the bus, "but now let's head for home."

"Get off, Garfield," yelled Jon, elbowing Garfield aside. "We're stopping soon. There's a place called The Golden Haven up ahead."

"Ah, a five-star hotel," chuckled Garfield. "I want the water bed!"

Garfield's eyes grew wide with disbelief as Jon pulled into a crowded campsite full of lorries, caravans, washing-lines and noisy children. Odie liked the place immediately and ran off to play with the other dogs. Jon seemed quite at home too, chatting to some bearded hippies who were building a bonfire.

"This is like an eating-too-much-too-fast-too-late-at-night nightmare," groaned Garfield, wandering round the site. "In fact," he added, his tummy churning like a cement mixer, "I wish it was!"

A delicious smell of warm stew drew Garfield towards a cauldron bubbling gently over an open fire.

"Hi, cat! Want some?" asked a friendly looking lady with earrings the size of dustbin lids. "You know our motto — what's yours is mine and what's mine is yours."

With a cry of delight, Garfield picked up the pot and tipped the entire contents down his throat.

"Bit heavy on the herbs," he burped, holding out the cauldron, "but quite pleasant. Got any more?"

The astonished woman grabbed a broom and chased Garfield to the next caravan. There he repeated his pathetic, hungry-looking cat routine until he was given more food. In this way, Garfield worked his way round the camp, eating everyone's supper.

"Maybe I like it here after all," he grinned.

By now, the bonfire had been lit and was crackling invitingly. Garfield found himself a cosy corner, curled up and went to sleep. He was rudely awakened by a loud twanging noise accompanied by a high-pitched whine.

"That sounds familiar," muttered Garfield, opening one eye. Silhouetted against the dancing flames, Garfield saw Jon with his battered guitar, singing a folk song.

" ♪ Where have all the bow ties gone?" he wailed. "Gone to young men wearing plaid socks, every one . . . ♫ "

Garfield put his paws over his ears and closed his eyes again. He did not see the audience pick Jon up and throw him boldly into the bus. Next moment, Garfield felt himself being picked up and dumped in there too, closely followed by Odie. The hippies slammed the door shut.

"Peace, man!" they called.

"I hardly think . . ." began Jon.

"No, no!" they yelled. "*We* want some! 'Bye!"

As the old coach rattled off into the night, Garfield gave a big smile of satisfaction. "Jon's bound to go home now," he chuckled.

"You know something, Garfield," called Jon from the driving seat. "This makes me all the more determined to go on. We don't need anyone but ourselves. We'll travel together — just the three of us — *forever!*"

Garfield was deciding between bursting into tears or suicide when a big car swept past, flashing its light and hooting urgently. Jon stopped the bus and his agent, Sinefield, leapt out of the car.

"I've looked *everywhere* for you!" he yelled.

"I'm not doing any more work," protested Jon.

"You don't have to for a while!" cried Sinefield, waving a cheque with a row of noughts like the wheels of a juggernaught lorry. "One of your cartoons has been syndicated world-wide. It's a best-seller!"

"But I have a dream . . ." said Jon.

"Me, too!" cried Garfield, snatching the cheque out of Sinefield's hand. "And this is gonna make it come true!"

A few days later, Garfield was sunning himself on the beach in Hawaii, surrounded by exotic tropical fruit. Jon was talking to a pretty girl in a grass skirt and Odie was splashing about in the pool.

"I've revised our thinking about the work ethic, Odie," said Garfield. "Work's okay — so long as it's done by other people, and they make lots of bucks!"

GARFIELD'S QUOTATIONS QUIZ

Here are some questions about well-known sayings. The first letter of each correct answer will fit into the grid at the end of the quiz and spell one of Garfield's quotable quotes.

1. Can you complete this quotation from HENRY FORD, the American car manufacturer, speaking about his 1920s Model T Ford?
"You can have any colour, so long as it's _ _ _ _ _."

2. Which of these catchphrases is associated with MAGNUS MAGNUSSON, the presenter of the TV quiz show *Mastermind*?
"Not many people know that."
"I've started so I'll finish."
"Yabbadabbadoo!"

3. Who wrote "Big brother is watching you!"?
BIG BROTHER
RICHARD ATTENBOROUGH
GEORGE ORWELL

4. "Never has so much been owed by so many to so few" is the slogan of the credit card company, AMERICAN EXPRESS.
True
False

5. Which of these catchphrases comes from the cult TV comedy show, MONTY PYTHON'S FLYING CIRCUS?
"What do you think of the show so far? Rubbish!"
"It's goodnight from me — and it's goodnight from him!"
"And now for something completely different."

6. The phrase "walls have ears" meaning "people could be listening to what you say" was a poster slogan during World War II.
True
False

7. In the old comedy films, was it LAUREL or HARDY who always said:
"Here's another fine mess you've gotten me into!"?

8. "Absence makes the heart grow fonder."
"Things that go bump in the night."
Nobody knows who wrote these well-known lines. What is the proper name for quotations of unknown origin?

9. Can you complete the famous last words of BEETHOVEN, the German composer, who went deaf in later life?
"_ _ _ _ _ _ _ _ _ _ in heaven."

10. Who wrote "You're a better man than I am, Gunga Din."?
GUNGA DIN'S SISTER
THE RUNNER-UP AT THE WORLD BODYBUILDING CHAMPIONSHIPS
RUDYARD KIPLING

11. Can you complete this famous proverb?

"Never put off till tomorrow what

___ ___ ___ __ _____."

12. According to the James Bond book (and film), these are "forever"; according to the old song, these are "a girl's best friend." What are they?

13. What does fictional detective, SHERLOCK HOLMES, say when he solves a difficult problem?
"I've got it!"
"Elementary, my dear Watson."
"Eat your heart out, Moriarty."

14. "Open Sesame!" is a quotation from the story of ALI BABA. To which famous book does the story belong?
ARABIAN NIGHTS
HARD DAY'S NIGHT
TALES OF BEATRIX POTTER

15. One of the best-known quotations of all times was uttered by Sir Henry Morton Stanley in 1871 in the heart of Africa. Can you complete it?
"Dr. _____, I presume."

GARFIELD'S QUOTABLE QUOTE

ANSWERS

The first letters of each answer spell: "BIG FAT HAIRY DEAL!"

15. Livingstone
14. Arabian Nights
13. "Elementary, my dear Watson."
12. Diamonds
11. "You can do today."
10. Rudyard Kipling
9. "I shall hear."
8. Anonymous
7. Hardy
6. True
5. "And now for something completely different."
4. False (it was said by Winston Churchill)
3. George Orwell
2. "I've started so I'll finish."
1. Black

In the 1991 Garfield annual, it was revealed that the name *Garfield* means:
"Dweller on the grassy land or pasture."
But what of the other names that Jim Davis chose for his characters — and the name Jim Davis itself? After another bout of exhaustive research, here's what they all mean . . .

Jon Arbuckle

Jon has recently established itself as an independent name, but originally it was a shortened form of *Jonathan*. It means "gift of the Lord." Both *Jon* and *Jonathan* have been widely used in America, the British preferring to stick with the more traditional *John*.

Arbuckle is a Scottish name originating from Airdrie in the old county of Lanarkshire. It comes from the Gaelic "ard an buachaille' which means "height of the shepherd." The first recorded use of the name was is 1499.

Given that Jon has doting parents who live on a farm in the country, his name is very appropriate — especially as Garfield dwells on the grassy land or pasture!

TOP TEN OTHER POSSIBLE MEANINGS FOR THE NAME "ARBUCKLE"

10. "pigeon-chested"
9. "rash giver"
8. "pudding-brained"
7. "man of socks"
6. "dances with cows"
5. "he who giggles in battle"
4. "Uh-oh, here he comes"
3. "royal bore"
2. "village dweeb"
1. "cat-pecked"

Hubert And Reba

Hubert is an old German name meaning "a bright or shining mind." It is rare as a first name these days, but is connected with a number of surnames including Hubbard (as in Old Mother Hubbard of nursery rhyme fame.)

During the 8th century, there was a *Saint Hubert* who was the patron saint of hunters. Perhaps that's why Hubert is always chasing Garfield out of his garden!

Reba is a shortened form of *Rebecca*, a very famous Hebrew name meaning "the captivator." A survey during the 1980s showed that *Rebecca* in its various forms was the fifth most popular name in the United Kingdom.

Arlene

Arlene is a variation of *Arline*, a name that did not come into use until the beginning of this century. There are two schools of thought about what it means. Some say *Arline* is a Gaelic word meaning "pledge." Others think the name is a corruption of *Charlene*, a German word meaning "strong and womanly." In either case, the descriptions fit Arlene very well — she is loyal to Garfield (despite his chauvenist indifference to her), and she is a girl who definitely knows her own mind!

Liz

Jon's would-be girlfriend, Liz the vet, has one of the best known names in the country — Elizabeth. Since the reign of Queen Elizabeth 1st (1558-1603), the name has been the third most popular in Britain. (The other two are *Mary* and *Ann*.) As well as *Liz*, *Elizabeth* has many other shortened forms including *Bess*, *Bessie*, *Beth*, *Betty*, *Eliza*, *Lisa*, *Elsie*, *Elsbeth* and *Libby* (to name but a few!) The name is of Hebrew origin and means "given to God."

Irma

Irma, the waitress at the restaurant often visited by Jon and Garfield, has a German name that means "the healer." *Irma* is actually a variant of *Emma*, another popular English forename. The name fits well with Irma's character because, despite working so hard that she is almost asleep on her feet, she will always lend a sympathetic ear to her customers' troubles.

ODIE AND NERMAL AREN'T LISTED — THEY'RE NOT IMPORTANT ENOUGH

Jim Davis

Jim is a shortened form of *James*. The name is of Hebrew origin and means "the supplanter." Along with its feminine form, *Jacqueline*, *James* is one of the most widely used names in the Western world.

Davis is a variant of *David*, another Hebrew name meaning "beloved." The name has been popular since Biblical times, King David being one of the greatest kings of ancient Israel.

Put together, Jim Davis's name means:

"The beloved supplanter."

What could be more apt? Jim Davis has supplanted all other cartoonists by creating Garfield, the world's most popular and widely read newspaper cartoon character.

Odie's I.Q. Test

To prove his theory that rocks evolved from dogs, Garfield devised an I.Q. test for Odie. It was a simple vocabulary test in which Odie had to write a sentence using a given word. He scored a massive zero, of course, and given that he's a dog, his answers give new meaning to the term "howlers" . . .

FOLDER
"In a bus or tube train, you should always give up your seat *folder* people."

AVOIDABLE
"In Spain, a skilled matador can easily *avoidable*."

COMMONPLACE
"Stop playing with that toy car, Tommy, and *commonplace* it on my desk."

WIGGLE
"I never go out on a windy day because I'm afraid my *wiggle* come off."

INSULATE
"Why did you get *insulate* last night?"

DECEIT
"The sofa's got a nasty stain on *deceit*."

AMMONIA
"*Ammonia* little boy, so I can't sit still all day."

JUICY
"Hey! *Juicy* what I just saw?"

BURDEN
"That Nature Reserve was a swizz — there wasn't a *burden* sight!"

DIPLOMA
The kitchen's flooded! Call *diploma*!"

JUNIOR
"In May you're watching The Cup Final; in *junior* watching Wimbledon."

AVENUE
"I *avenue* car."

BULLETIN
"During the battle, the soldier got a *bulletin* his arm."

FALSIFY
"If I build a card castle, it *falsify* move."

CANADA
"I'd like a bar of chocolate, a packet of crisps and a *canada* cheapest cola."

FORFEIT
"Animals with *forfeit* run faster than those with two."

ANTIDOTE
"I get lots of money because my *antidotes* on me."

THRONG
"That's the *throng* answer, you thilly!"

DAISIES
"Peter's such a pest, I dread the *daisies* at home."

TORONTO
"When you're playing rounders, you have *toronto* first base, then second base . . ."

ODIE'S TOP TEN CONFUSED CLICHES

10. In one nostril and out the other
9. Caught with his head in the cookie jar
8. All dressed up and no place to drool
7. Cold hands, warm liver
6. I'll be a donkey's uncle
5. His breath is worse than his bite
4. Between a rock and a hard-boiled egg
3. A new leash on life
2. Keep a stiff rubber lip
1. Two tongues are better than one

NEVER A DULL

MOMENT

THERE'S NOTHING LIKE A QUIET EVENING AT HOME

CLICK

CLICK
CLICK
CLICK
CLICK

1988 United Feature Syndicate, Inc.

GOBBLE GOBBLE GOBBLE...

DONK!

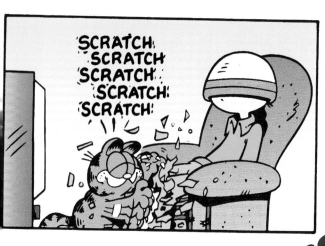

SCRATCH
SCRATCH
SCRATCH
SCRATCH
SCRATCH

NOT AROUND HERE, AT ANY RATE

JIM DAVIS 1-24

**CATS DON'T ASK,
CATS TAKE!**

Garfield's Guide To Shakespeare

Garfield dispenses some essential advice on avoiding being bored by the Bard.

Playtime Is Prime

Another survival strategy in the theatre is to make proper use of the interval. As soon as you hear a final rhyming couplet, shoot out of your seat and power your way down the line of pre-ordered drinks and snacks awaiting collection in the refreshment area. You can be back in your seat with an ice-cream before anyone says, ''who's been eating my smoked salmon?'' (A less energetic alternative is to put on your own production with an interval at the end of every scene — or speech.)

This Is The Works!

As sure as lasagne's lasagne, your aunt or granny will give you a copy of *The Complete Works Of William Shakespeare* at about the age of 12. They'll say, ''You won't want this now, but it'll come in really useful later on.'' This is a lie! The book is totally unreadable. Each page is printed in two columns of microscopic print that gives you chronic double vision about halfway through the first act of *A Midsummer Night's Dream*. But a word of advice — DON'T THROW THIS BOOK AWAY! Keep it in the lounge for squashing spiders, or in the kitchen for reaching the cookie jar.

What's In A Name?

Shakespeare wrote comedies, tragedies and histories. These names are a bit confusing because the comedies are pretty tragic (mix-ups, mistaken identities — that sort of stuff), and the tragedies are a hoot.

Perchance To Dream

Never go to see a professional production of a Shakespeare play. Good actors make gestures, pull faces and emphasise the important words so that you get the gist of what is going on. This keeps you awake. You are much better off to go to an amateur production in which nobody understands a word they're saying. Then you can sleep through the entire performance.

26

(I mean — get real! If you're some wealthy big shot, you're not going to lose it all because you're a bit stressed. You'd have six months in the Seychelles, or *eat* your way out of trouble.) The history plays are okay if you're into Medieval English history. If you like Bauering or R.E.M., they're not so hot. The battle scenes are a terrible con because they always take place off stage — people just rush in and out, just telling you about them. If you want to see some ancient battle action, hire a *Rocky* video.

All Dressed Up And Nowhere To Go

People are fond of putting on Shakespeare plays in modern dress. There's usually some arty reason for this, but really it's because they don't want the expense of proper historical costumes. Watching King Lear performed in army surplus or Macbeth in boiler suits doesn't make them any more comprehensible — it's what the guys SAY that needs modernisation. Check this out —

ROMEO: How's it hanging, baby-cakes?

JULIET: Pretty cool.

ROMEO: Wanna lip-wrestle?

JULIET: Get a life, sucker. What's the drop?

ROMEO: We've got probs. My brothers are askin' and your brothers are startin'. They'll all get decked!

What do you reckon, then? Instant access or what? Someone tell the R.S.C.

The Garfield Shakespearean Folio

If you think about it, Bill and I have something in common — we've both given the world some memorable quotes. Here are a couple of his throwaway one-liners:

"Uneasy lies the head that wears a crown."

"We are such stuff as dreams are made on."

And here's some of my famous worldly wisdom:

"Patience is waiting for the pizza to thaw."

"You know it's Monday when you discover a land mine in your breakfast."

Now if you put our amazing talents together, you get this:

The Garfield Macbeth
"Is this a pizza which I see before me?"

The Garfield Hamlet
"To eat or not to eat: that is a stupid question."

The Garfield Henry the Vth
"Once more onto the beach, dear friends. Once more!"

The Garfield Twelfth Night
"Some men are born geeks, some achieve geekiness, and some have geekiness thrust upon them."

Pretty darn cute, huh?

Epilogue

I looked all through Jon's copy of *The Complete Works* for a suitable quote to round off this guide, but both Odies kept interrupting me and all four Jons called me over for supper . . .

I HATE FEBRUARY

FEBRUARY STARTS OUT IRRITATING, BECOMES BORING AND ENDS UP DEPRESSING

FEBRUARY IS THE "MONDAY" OF MONTHS

JIM DAVIS 2-8

MOST KIDS LOVE SNOW

MOST KIDS LOVE BUILDING FORTS AND THROWING SNOWBALLS

MINE ARE OUT FOR WORLD DOMINATION

JIM DAVIS 2-12

IF JON'S NOT GOING TO LET US IN, I SAY WE BREAK THE DOOR IN!

TAP

IT'S TOUGH BUILDING UP A FULL HEAD OF STEAM IN DEEP SNOW

JIM DAVIS 2-13

BE YOUR OWN

BEST FRIEND

SOUND
THE ALARM !

RISING
STARS!

NOW PLAYING
IN A PERCOLATOR
NEAR YOU

The Garfield Fact File On
COFFEE

Coffee is the world's second most valuable product. Only oil generates more money on the international market.

Brazil is the world's largest exporter of coffee. (There's an awful lot of coffee in Brazil!) Neighbouring Colombia is second, with Indonesia and West Africa joint third.

The United States of America is the biggest importer of coffee, but this is partly due to the huge size of the country. On a per-cups per-day basis, the Scandinavian countries of Norway, Sweden and Denmark drink the most coffee.

Coffee is made from coffee beans. These are found inside the red, cherry-like berries of the coffee tree.

Coffee berries are picked by hand by workers on the plantations. Machines remove the beans from the berries and these are washed and dried to remove their silvery outer skins. Then the green insides are roasted to produce the aromatic brown beans that make coffee.

Legend has it that coffee was discovered about 1,000 years ago by an Ethiopian goatherd called Kaldi. His goats began leaping about after eating the red berries of a nearby tree. Kaldi took some of the berries to a nearby monastery where the monks used them to make a drink. The monks were very grateful because the new drink kept them awake during their long hours of prayer.

A true story tells how coffee was taken to South America. In 1723, a French naval officer called Captain De Clieu took a small coffee tree on board his ship bound for the island of Martinique in the Caribbean. Water ran short during the long voyage, but De Clieu sacrificed his own ration to keep the tree alive. Eventually, it was planted and grew into a flourishing tree whose seeds were taken to mainland South America. Every coffee tree growing there today is descended from Captain De Clieu's original.

Two London insitutions began life as coffee houses. Jonathan's Coffee House in Change Alley, frequented by stockbrokers, eventually became the London Stock Exchange. Ship owners and insurers used to meet in Edward Lloyd's coffee house in Lombard Street and this became Lloyds of London, the centre of world marine insurance.

If you can't stand the caffeine, stay out of the kitchen!

Two Coffee Recipes

TOP TEN WAYS GARFIELD LIKES HIS COFFEE

10. Hot
9. Hair-free
8. Non-crunchy
7. One barrel at a time
6. Doughnut-ready
5. So caffeinated it jumps out of the cup and slaps him
4. Sucked straight out of the filter
3. Intravenously
2. Strong enough to sit up and bark
1. With a 12-course breakfast

Iced Coffee

16 teaspoons coffee granules
2 teaspoons vanilla essence
30g sugar
1 litre water
½ litre milk
Whipped cream
Cinnamon powder
Chocolate powder
Ground nutmeg

Dissolve the coffee granules in the water, stirring well. Add the sugar and vanilla essence. Leave the mixture in the fridge for 24 hours. To serve, fill half a glass with coffee mixture and fill almost to the top with milk. Add a spoonful of whipped cream and decorate with a sprinkling of the spices and chocolate powder.

Coffee Oatmeal Muffins

100g self-raising flour
100g rolled oats
100g chopped almonds
50g butter
120 ml strong black coffee
120 ml milk
2 tablespoons clear honey
½ teaspoon salt

Sift the flour into a bowl. Add the oats and salt and mix together. Melt the butter, honey and coffee in a saucepan and stir in the milk. Heat until almost boiling, but do not allow to boil. Add the dry ingredients and the almonds and mix thoroughly. Place spoonfuls of the mixture onto a greased baking tray and cook in a preheated oven at 200°C/Gas Mark 6 for 30 minutes. Leave for five minutes to cool, then turn out onto a cake rack. Serve warm or cold. (Makes about 12).

Photograph, information and recipies kindly supplied by The Coffee Information Centre, 21 Berners Street, London.

PLEASE REMEMBER

You should always have parental permission to use the kitchen, or a grown-up with you when you're cooking.

35

GARFIELD'S SPOOKY BELIEVE IT OR DON'T

Five of these amazing supernatural stories actually happened. The other three are completely made up. Can you find the frauds?

1. HOUSE OF HORRORS

Harlow House in Essex must rank as Britain's most haunted house. During its 200 year history, there have been sightings of a headless nun, a phantom stagecoach and mysterious messages that appear and disappear on the wall. As well as that, organ music has often been heard and there is a resident poltergeist who throws objects around. The house is so scary to live in that nobody has stayed there for more than a year and it is now falling into disrepair through neglect.

2. NORTHWEST PASSAGE

In 1928, the captain of a ship crossing the Atlantic saw a man standing in the room next to his cabin. The ship did not carry passengers and it was not one of the crew, so the captain suspected a stowaway. But the man suddenly disappeared, leaving a message written on the wall: "Steer to the northwest." The captain was so amazed by his visitor that he changed course as requested. A few hours later, he came upon a sinking ship whose only survivor was the man he had seen earlier. The man said he had fallen asleep through exhaustion and had dreamed about being rescued.

3. POETIC JUSTICE

When Dante, the famous Italian poet, died in 1321, the manuscript of the last part of his great poem, *The Divine Comedy*, was missing. Nobody could find it until Dante appeared to his son, Jacopo, in a vision, indicating a small window with a blind in front of it. When Jacopo looked behind the blind, he found the final part of the poem.

4. GHOST SHIP

Everyone has heard of the Mary Celeste, the ship found drifting in the Atlantic in 1872 with no sign of life on board. Less well known is the case of the Northern Belle, a ghost ship that appeared in no less than 17 different countries. The latest and most famous sighting took place in Australia in 1972. Holidaymakers on a Sydney beach saw the ship, an 18th Century schooner with a distinctive flag, appear over the horizon and sail towards them — only to disappear in the spray thrown up by the big, rolling waves.

5. A MOVING STORY

It is traditional for ghosts to haunt a particular place, but this one moved house! During the 1880s, a woman in a long black dress, holding a handkerchief, appeared several times in a house in Cheltenham, Gloucestershire. Eventually, the appearances ceased but, nearly 70 years later in 1958, the same black figure with a handkerchief was seen in a flat several houses down the street.

6. NEVER A CROSS WORD

In 1944, the Allies were preparing to invade Nazi-occupied Europe. At the same time, Leonard Dawe, a 54 year old teacher, was compiling the *Daily Telegraph* crossword. He came up with a series of clues that appeared to be tipping the Germans off about D-Day. He even mentioned the word OVERLORD, the code-name for the whole invasion. But, when questioned, Dawe had absolutely no knowledge whatsoever about the Allies' plans.

7. PHANTOM BANTAM

A recent ghostly going-on took place in Indiana, USA, in April 1995. An American artist, A. R. Buckle, brought home a cockerel from his parents' farm, but the bird was immediately eaten by the man's greedy cat. Even so, the cockerel can be heard crowing at dawn every day.

8. ALL DAY LONG THE NOISE OF BATTLE ROLLED

In August 1951, two English women on holiday near Dieppe in France were awakened by the sound of gunfire. The battle lasted for three hours and the women were so astonished that they wrote down every sound they heard. There was no war that day, but their description almost exactly matches the Allied raid on Dieppe in August 1942 in which over 3,000 soldiers were killed or wounded.

The following stories are false: Numbers 1, 4 and 7

CLICK!

WHAT IS IT, GARFIELD?! IS THERE A THIEF? IS THE HOUSE ON FIRE?

WORSE! THE LIGHT IN THE REFRIGERATOR IS OUT!

ODIE DRIPS SO MUCH MAYBE I SHOULD CALL A PLUMBER!

PANT PANT

THAT'S A FIGURE OF SPEECH, GARFIELD

DRIP
DRIP
DRIP
DRIP
DRIP
DRIP
DRIP

SQUEAK

FUN, ANYONE?

HERE'S LOOKING AT ME, KID!

FUTURE KITTY

"Shall I read you another King Arthur story, Garfield?" asked Jon.
"ZZZZZZZZZZ!" snored Garfield
"Let's listen to my *Music For Geeks* tape again," suggested Jon.
"ZZZZZZZZZ!" snored Garfield.
"I suppose we could have our picnic tea early," said Jon.
"Now you're talkin'!" cried Garfield, sitting bolt upright, bright-eyed and alert.
As Jon opened the basket, Garfield produced Pooky.
"A teddy bear's picnic, eh?" chuckled Jon. "How cute!"
Garfield grabbed all the sandwiches, whisked them under Pooky's nose and swallowed the whole lot in one big gulp.
"Pooky was hungry," he burped.
Jon and Garfield were on holiday in England. They were touring the West Country in a hired car, visiting places of historical interest. It was Midsummer's Eve, and they were parked at the foot of a grassy hill, site of King Arthur's castle, Camelot. The rain beat down, drumming on the roof of the car and dancing on the bonnet like diamonds.
"I expect you're wondering why we're here, Garfield," said Jon.
"If this is a philosophical question," muttered Garfield, "I've cracked it. 'I eat, sleep and watch TV — therefore, I am!' "
"We're here," continued Jon, his voice dropping to an excited whisper, "because, tonight, they say the Knights Of The Round Table ride round the hill."
"I hate pageants!" exclaimed Garfield. "Let's hit town."
"We're staying here all night," said Jon, grabbing Garfield's arm, " to catch a glimpse of them."
Suddenly, the rain stopped, like someone turning off a shower.
"Come on, Garfield!" yelled Jon, leaping out of the car. "Race you to the top!"
Half an hour later, as Garfield dragged himself and Pooky to the summit, the heavens opened up again.
"When I catch up with Jon," spluttered Garfield, "*he'll* be history!"

Garfield wandered round the desolate hilltop, half-blinded by the driving rain. During a particularly vivid flash of lightning, he saw something glinting in the distance. He thought it was Jon's torch, but moments later Jon came running up from the opposite direction.

"This way, you guys," he called. "I've found a cave where we can take shelter."

Inside the cave, Garfield shook himself dry (making Jon even wetter than before) and wandered off to explore.

"Why do you keep pressing the walls, Garfield!" asked Jon.

"Looking for a built-in fridge or drinks dispenser," explained Garfield.

"If you're hungry," said Jon, "you can have all these tins of hot dog sausages. I brought them for a midnight feast."

Garfield raced over and held out his paw.

"Yeah! Gimme five!" whooped Jon, slapping it.

"I want the tin opener, nerd-features," growled Garfield, miming the action of opening a tin.

"I d-d-didn't bring a tin-opener, Garfield," stammered Jon.

"Sometimes, you make Odie look bright," declared Garfield.

Then Garfield remembered what he had seen during the lightning flash.

"Hang loose, buddy," he called, hurrying past Jon with a wave. Garfield scampered over the hill until he reached a big stone with a sword sticking out of it.

"Should make light work of a few tins," he chuckled, grabbing the hilt. As Garfield started to pull, the storm stopped and the hilltop was bathed in soft, yellow moonlight.

The sword slid out of the stone like oiled silk. Garfield held it aloft. Instantly, he found himself clothed in shining armour.

"I am King Garfield Of The Round Pizza!" he proclaimed in a voice that everyone could hear. "Rightful successor to mighty King Arthur and new Ruler Of This Realm!"

As he finished speaking, a stream of Knights came riding over the hill. They had plumes and shields of dazzling colours and rode on fiery, snorting steeds. The knights surrounded Garfield, dismounted and knelt down before him.

"We pledge thee our allegiance, Sire," they chorused.

"That's cool," said Garfield. "Where's the celebration banquet?"

The knights looked round and, following their gaze, Garfield saw the walls of Camelot castle rising up out of the mist-enshrouded ground. The drawbridge was lowered and the unmistakable figure of Sir Lancelot emerged, smiling and beckoning.

"What are we waiting for, guys," cried Garfield. "LET'S PARTY!"

For the next three hours, Garfield commanded a stream of sweating servants who hurried in and out with huge wooden platters piled high with food. Eventually, even King Garfield was full. He sprawled across his throne, waiting to be entertained.

"Fetch the royal TV!" he ordered.

Sir Lancelot scratched his head and everyone else looked baffled.

"Okay, okay. Make it the minstrel guy," sighed Garfield. Lancelot clapped his hands.

"Summon Geeko The Meek," he called.

"That name sounds familiar," thought Garfield.

Garfield gasped with amazement as Geeko stepped nervously from behind a curtain, holding his lute. It was Jon! He was wearing a green and yellow quartered outfit, long pointed shoes and a cap with bells on the end.

"Smartest he's looked for years!" commented Garfield.

"My liege," cried Jon, bowing low to Garfield. "I give you my latest ballad . . .

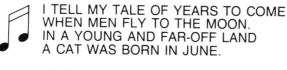

I TELL MY TALE OF YEARS TO COME
WHEN MEN FLY TO THE MOON.
IN A YOUNG AND FAR-OFF LAND
A CAT WAS BORN IN JUNE.

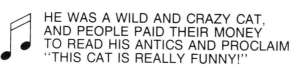

HE WAS A WILD AND CRAZY CAT,
AND PEOPLE PAID THEIR MONEY
TO READ HIS ANTICS AND PROCLAIM
"THIS CAT IS REALLY FUNNY!"

"I like this song!" interrupted Garfield. "Gimme some more."

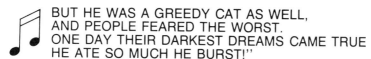

BUT HE WAS A GREEDY CAT AS WELL,
AND PEOPLE FEARED THE WORST.
ONE DAY THEIR DARKEST DREAMS CAME TRUE
HE ATE SO MUCH HE BURST!"

"ENOUGH!" roared Garfield, leaping to his feet. "Take the varlet away and throw him in the dungeons. I'll *never* be defeated by a dinner!"

Garfield sat back on his throne, huffing and puffing with indignation.

"Let me soothe your savage brow," said another familiar voice.

"Make way for the Lady, Queen Arlenevere!" announced Sir Lancelot.

"You look ridiculous in that pointed hat," said Garfield.

"Is my lord a bit grumpy-wumpy, then?" teased Arlene, tickling Garfield under the chin.

"Don't touch the King's person," snapped Garfield. "And get a portcullis in that gap in your teeth."

"You've got to stop insulting me, Garfield," said Arlene.

"Why change the habits of a lifetime?" retorted Garfield.

"Because I'm your Queen," exclaimed Arlene.

"You mean . . .?" gasped Garfield, suddenly going pale.

"That's right, buddy boy," chuckled Arlene. "We're married now."

A nightmare vision of kittens and washing-up flashed in front of Garfield's eyes, only to be shattered by a thunderous knocking on the door. It burst open and in strode a blue knight, carrying a sack over his shoulder and wearing a peaked cap instead of a helmet.

"And who, pray, are you?" asked Garfield. ("As if I don't know!")

"I am your lifetime enemy and mortal foe, Sir Mordred Of The Mail," exclaimed the knight.

"Well, deliver your letters and hop it, buster," said Garfield. "You're a bit of a party-pooper."

"I'm not here to deliver letters," roared Sir Mordred. "I'm here to deliver a CHALLENGE!"

"What, like Anneka Rice?" suggested Garfield. "Build a 50ft stone castle in a weekend — that sort of stuff?"

"I challenge you to a joust!" bellowed Mordred.

"Oh, I see," said Garfield. "What's green and hairy and goes up and down? A caterpillar . . ."

"Joust, Garfield," whispered Arlene, "not jest."

"I heard what he said," replied Garfield.

Sir Lancelot hurried over, an anxious look on his face.

"You cannot refuse his challenge, Sire," he exclaimed. "You must fight for the honour of your Realm."

"Take a hike, pal," said Garfield, folding his arms.

"Then fight for *my* honour, Garfield," urged Arlene. "Knights always joust for the favour of their ladies."

"Get real, honeybunch," answered Garfield.

"Do I take it you're refusing my challenge?" called Sir Mordred.

"Got it in one, buddy boy," replied Garfield.

"Then," spat Mordred, "You are no more a king than THIS!"

Sir Mordred held up Pooky.

"Where did you get him from?" demanded Garfield.

"This worthless plaything?" sneered Mordred. "I found it outside a cave over yonder."

"Hand him over!" ordered Garfield.

"Certainly not," laughed Garfield's enemy. "I intend to use him for archery practice."

Garfield felt the red mist rising behind his eyes.

"Listen, pal," he hissed. "That little guy is my lifelong friend."

"Pah!" scoffed Sir Mordred. "The King's companion is a pathetic, stuffed animal!"

"GGGRRRRR!" raged Garfield, charging straight at his foe, shoulder-down like an American footballer. BLAM! Garfield hit Mordred in the stomach, sending him rolling backwards out of the door. There was a short pause followed by a satisfying SPLASH as Sir Mordred Of The Mail landed in the moat.

"That's *stamped* my authority on him!" chuckled Garfield, dusting his paws.

After this, everything happened very fast. Garfield was hoisted aloft by the cheering crowd and carried triumphantly round the great hall of Camelot. The victorious monarch ordered another celebration banquet that went on throughout the night. Garfield was just popping his final sugared fig into his mouth when he noticed everything starting to fade.

"What's going on?" he cried.

Looking out of the dissolving window, Garfield saw the first pale streaks of dawn creeping over the horizon.

"Midsummer's Eve is over!" he gasped.

Moments later, Garfield found himself sitting on the bare hilltop again. His armour had disappeared, along with Camelot and all his new-found friends. All he had left was Pooky.

"Let's see if Jon's in the cave, l'il buddy," said Garfield. "He can fix breakfast."

Sure enough, Jon lay curled up in a corner, fast asleep.

"I expect he'll come up with some corny line that he dreamt I was King of Camelot," muttered Garfield. Then he noticed Jon's lute leaning against the wall. He kicked Jon awake and pointed to it urgently.

"Something strange happened last night, Garfield," began Jon. "I was your minstrel . . ."

"I know all that," interrupted Garfield, hiding the lute behind a rock. "Just don't play it again. You were TERRIBLE!"

As they drove away in the early morning sunshine, Jon explained that he had escaped via a secret passage that led from his cell to the cave.

"And I met someone the spitting image of our mailman," he added. "Boy, was he mad! Is it true that you'd only fight for the honour of your teddy?"

Garfield nodded proudly.

"You gotta have priorities," he said.